Teacher Teacher Jokes

Jokes by Tony McMylor
Cover by Paul Crompton
Cartoons by Walter Howarth

Copyright © 1991 World International Publishing Ltd.

All rights reserved. Published in Great Britain by
World International Publishing Ltd.,
an Egmont Company, Egmont House,
P.O. Box 111, Great Ducie Street,
Manchester M60 3BL.
Printed in Great Britain.

British Library Cataloguing in Publication Data
McMylor, Tony
   Teacher, teacher joke book.
   1. Humorous prose
   I. Title II. McAleer, Joyce
   828.91402

ISBN 0 7498 0446 7

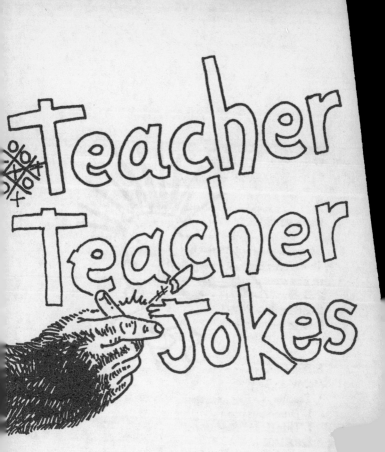

Teacher Teacher Jokes

World International Publishing
Limited Manchester

Stuart: 'Dad, will you help me find the lowest common denominator in this problem?'
Dad: 'Haven't they found that yet? They were looking for it when I was at school.'

Teacher: 'Jonathan, are you eating a sweet?'
Jonathan: 'No, Miss, it's a gumboil.'
Teacher: 'Well, wait until playtime and then hand them round.'

Amy: 'How many teachers work at this school?'
Jamie: 'About half of them.'

Teacher: 'Alison, why are you scratching yourself?'
Alison: 'It's easier than trying to get someone else to do it, Miss.'

Mum: 'Kevin's teacher says we ought to buy him an encyclopedia.'
Dad: 'Let him walk to school like I had to.'

Teacher: 'In what part of the world are the people the most ignorant?'

Simon: 'Tokyo, Sir.'

Teacher: 'Why do you say that?'

Simon: 'My geography book says that's where the population is the densest.'

Stephen: 'Dad, what do you get if you add four grapes and three grapes?'

Dad: 'Surely you can do a simple sum like that yourself.'

Stephen: 'No, I can't; we always use carrots at school.'

Mum: 'How was the maths exam, Katie? Could you manage all the questions?'

Katie: 'Yes, Mum, I'd no trouble with the questions . . . but the answers were a lot harder.'

Teacher: 'Harold, which month has twenty-eight days?'

Harold: 'All of them, Sir.'

Teacher: 'Jason, how can you prove that the earth is round?'

Jason: 'It wasn't me who said it was, Sir.'

Stevenson: 'Sir, I don't think I deserve none out of ten for this test.'

Teacher: 'Neither do I, Stevenson, but it's the lowest mark I can give you.'

New teacher: 'Why do you keep on referring to this school as the blood bank?'

Old teacher: 'Because it's full of clots.'

'Name four members of the cat family that you can see at the zoo.'

'A lion and three tigers, Miss.'

Teacher: 'Greenwood, stop trying to run the class. Do you think you are the teacher?'

Greenwood: 'No, Sir.'

Teacher: 'Then stop behaving like an idiot.'

Teacher: 'Late again, Wilson.'

Wilson: 'Sorry, Sir, I overslept.'

Teacher: 'You mean to tell me you sleep at home as well?'

Teacher: 'If you had ten pence in one pocket and fifty pence in the other, what would you have?'

Eric: 'Please, Sir . . . somebody else's trousers on.'

Teacher: 'Which is farther away – Australia or the moon?'

Roger: 'Australia, Sir.'

Teacher: 'Are you sure?'

Roger: 'Yes, Sir. I can see the moon, but I can't see Australia.'

Teacher: 'Has the death rate in Britain changed since Medieval times?'

Sparks: 'No, Sir, it's still one death per person.'

Susie: 'Miss, I've added this list of numbers eight times.'

Miss: 'And what do you get?'

Susie: 'Eight different answers.'

Physics teacher: 'How many balls of string would it take to reach the moon?'

Ronnie: 'Just one great big long one, Sir.'

Teacher: 'What is the
highest form
of animal life
on earth?'
Willie: 'The giraffe.'

Woodwork teacher: 'What are you making,
Brown?'
Brown: 'A rabbit hutch, Sir.'
Woodwork teacher: 'And what is this mess here,
Smith?'
Smith: 'I'm making the sawdust for Brown's
rabbit hutch.'

Science teacher: 'The formula for water, Carter.'
Carter: 'Er . . . er . . . H,I,J,K,L,M,N,O, Sir.'
Science teacher: 'That is ridiculous. Where did
you get that answer from?'
Carter: 'Regan, Sir . . . he said it was H to O.'

Teacher: 'What are you making, Stanley?'
Stanley: 'A portable, Sir.'
Teacher: 'A portable what?'
Stanley: 'Dunno yet. I've only made the handles.'

'What family does the hippopotamus belong to?'
  'Dunno, Miss, nobody in our street has got one.'

Teacher: 'How many feet are there in a yard?'
Patrick: 'Would that be a backyard or a schoolyard, Miss?'

Sidebottom: 'When I leave school I want to join the police force and follow in my father's footsteps.'
Careers master: 'I didn't know your father was a policeman.'
Sidebottom: 'He's not, he's a burglar.'

Art teacher: 'Darren, what is pop-art?'
Darren: 'That's what me Dad says to me Mum when he's just going to pop-art for a minute.'

Cheeky kid: 'Sir, have you ever painted anyone in the nude?'
Art teacher: 'Only once, but I left my socks on so that I'd have somewhere to stick my brushes.'

Maths teacher: 'How many fingers have you?'
Jonathan: 'Ten, Miss.'
Maths teacher: 'And if the doctor cut four of them off, what would you have?'
Jonathan: 'A good excuse to pack in my piano lessons.'

'My teacher must like me, she keeps putting kisses on all my sums.'

R.I. teacher: 'Do you say your prayers before meals, Simon?'
Simon: 'Only before school dinners. My mother is a good cook.'

Jenkins: 'I want to be in the big-time like my dad.'
Careers master: 'What does he do?'
Jenkins: 'He mends town hall clocks and church clocks.'

Teacher: 'I wish you'd pay a little attention, Phillip.'
Phillip: 'I'm paying as little as I can, Sir.'

Games master: 'Come here. I'll teach you to throw stones at Parkinson.'
Scroggins: 'I wish you would, Sir. I keep missing him.'

'If we breathe oxygen during the day, what do we breathe at night?'
'Nitrogen.'

R.I. teacher: 'Where do you find the Book of Numbers?'
Ruth: 'In a telephone kiosk, Sir.'

The headmaster was busy reading the racing page in his office when the telephone rang. His secretary answered it.
'It's a long distance from California,' she said.
'Yes, I know it is,' he answered.

Willie: 'Why are your mum and dad learning Italian?'
Millie: 'They've adopted an Italian baby and they want to be able to understand him when he learns to talk.'

Prof. Blank: 'Have you a brother who did this course last year?'

Student: 'No, Sir, that was me; I'm re-taking it.'

Prof. Blank: 'My word . . . amazing resemblance.'

'Where are elephants found?'

'Well, with memories like they've got, they hardly ever get lost.'

Teacher: 'At which battle did Lord Nelson die?'

Tommy: 'His last one, Sir.'

Chemistry teacher: 'What are nitrates?'

Johnnie: 'Time and a half, I think, Sir.'

Teacher: 'You missed school yesterday, didn't you, Grubb?'

Grubb: 'Not a lot, Miss.'

Teacher: 'What do four and six make, Alvin?'

Alvin: 'Dunno, Sir.'

Teacher: 'It's ten, isn't it?'

Alvin: 'No, Sir, five and five is ten.'

Teacher: 'Can anyone tell me what a slug is?'
Clevercloggs: 'Yes, Sir, it's a snail that's been evicted.'

Caretaker: 'And just *how* did you break the classroom window, Scroggins?'
Scroggins: 'I was just cleaning my catapult and it went off.'

Teacher: 'Peter, give me a sentence beginning with "I".'
Peter: 'I is . . .'
Teacher: 'No, no, boy, begin it "I am".'
Peter: 'Okay, I am the ninth letter of the alphabet.'

Knock! Knock!
Who's there?
Warren.
Warren who?
Warren old fusspot our teacher is.

Knock! Knock!
Who's there?
Michael.
Michael who?
Michael do your homework if you give him 10p.

Knock! Knock!
Who's there?
Evadne.
Evadne who?
Evadne haemwork for a week, the noo.

Knock! Knock!
Who's there?
Conrad.
Conrad who?
Conrad no homework, either.

Knock! Knock!
Who's there?
Samuel.
Samuel who?
Samuel help me with my homework, won't you?

Knock! Knock!
Who's there?
Gwenfrew.
Gwenfrew who?
Gwenfrew the stone that broke the classroom window.

Knock! Knock!
Who's there?
Howell.
Howell who?
Howell I get to school? I've lost my bus pass!

Knock! Knock!
Who's there?
Leopold.
Leopold who?
Leopold more votes than you did in the school election.

Selections from the school library

Totem Poles *by Calvin Wood*
Bridge *by Clifton Suspension*
The Betrothal *by Marius Vicker*
Passing Exams *by Marcus Hyley*
Erase Your Mistakes *by Reuben Outt*
Volunteering *by Shamus Intowitt*
First Violin Lessons *by Walter Wrackett*
Nature Walks *by Wanda Round*
Negative Thinking *by Mona Lott*
Looking After Your Money *by Owen Cash*
Birdwatching *by Thomasina Wren*

Great Sea Tragedies *by Mandy Boats*
Great Sporting Venues *by Jocelyn Krowds*
Collecting Model Infantrymen *by Aled Soulger*
Ready For Take Off *by Jock Saway*
The Castaway *by Levi N. Drigh*
Competitive Weight Lifting *by Hugh Jarms*
I Am A Ghost *by Esau Froomy*
Beaten Black And Blue *by Bruce Eezilly*
Kite Flying *by Augusta Wind*
The Bargain Holiday *by Audrey Turlly*
How To Speak Clearly *by Artie Q. Late*
We Are Guilty *by Angus F. U. Must*
Follow The Flock *by Zina Ramsbottom*

More selections from the school library

A professor of physics named Hackle,
Was demonstrating the block and the tackle.
While consulting his book,
He was caught by the hook,
And his language quite made the air crackle.

An 'A' Level student from Hull,
Thought French was exceedingly dull.
Till, when visiting Rheims,
He met the girl of his dreams,
And found that it really was useful.

'Did you hear about the cross-eyed teacher who couldn't control his pupils?'

Eric: 'I got 78% in the maths exam and still
       didn't pass.'
Dad: '78% and you didn't pass? How's that?'
Eric: 'The correct answer was 84%.'

'What's the difference between lightning and electricity?'
   'You don't get bills for lightning.'

R.I. teacher: 'Hands up all those who wish to go to Heaven.'

All the class raise their hands except little Orson.

R.I. teacher: 'Don't you want to go to Heaven, Orson?'

Orson: 'Please, Miss, me mam said I've got to go straight home.'

Teacher: 'Stanley, what is water?'

Stanley: 'Water is a colourless liquid, chemical formula H_2O. And it turns black when I put my hands in it.'

Teacher: 'Conrad, if you washed twenty five cars and the owners each gave you fifty pence, what would you have?'

Conrad: 'A pocketful of change and an aching arm, Sir.'

Headmaster: 'Yes, Mr Carstairs, your son will definitely go down in history.'

Mr Carstairs: 'Oh?'

Headmaster: '. . . and in French . . . and in German . . . and in geography!'

'Where do people go to learn to become philosophers?'

'A school of thought.'

'Where do you go to learn about horseshoes and rabbit's feet?'

'A charm school.'

'Where did Sir Lancelot get his education?'

'Knight school.'

'Where do odd children go to get straightened out?'

'Evening classes.'

'Where do spies go to learn to fly?'
    'To a secret aerial college.'

'Where do locksmiths learn their trade?'
    'Yale.'

'Where do joiners send their sons?'
    'To boarding school.'

'Which public school did Robin Hood go to?'
    ' 'Arrow.'

Did you hear about the school where the pupils went on strike until the headmaster agreed to a school trip?

He stretched a wire across the top of the steps just before the bell rang to end lessons.

Dopey Davidson enjoyed it so much, that when he was discharged from hospital, he asked if they could have another one next year.

Drama teacher: 'Give me the name of a famous straight actress who often plays royalty?'
Orson: 'Ruler Lenska.'

Teacher: 'Maxwell, what is a paragon?'
Maxwell: 'A dead sky-diver, Sir.'

Dan: 'Did you know that our biology teacher has started keeping birds of prey?'
Sam: 'Does he have trouble getting them to kneel down?'

Rickie: 'Mickey, stop jumping up and down.'
Mickey: 'I can't. Teacher just gave me my medicine and she didn't shake the bottle.'

Sandy: 'Why weren't you in class this morning?'
Andy: 'I had to go to the dentist.'
Sandy: 'Is your tooth still hurting?'
Andy: 'Dunno — I left it with the dentist.'

Jonathan: 'Your gym socks have got holes in
them.'
Amy: 'They have not.'
Jonathan: 'They must have or you wouldn't be
able to get your feet in.'

Simon: 'I was an unwanted child.'
Teacher: 'Why do you say that?'
Simon: 'My mum said she always wanted a
cocker spaniel.'

Daniel: 'I've just knocked the caretaker's ladder
over.'
Louise: 'Hadn't you better tell him then?'
Daniel: 'He already knows. He was up it at the
time.'

Carole: 'He's a tough-looking bloke, this new
needlework teacher, isn't he?'
Paula: 'Yes, but he sews fantastic mailbags.'

Peterson: 'Sir, I have a question.'
Teacher: 'Yes?'
Peterson: 'You know that you said if you hold a shell up to your ear you can hear the sea?'
Teacher: 'Well, what's the question?'
Peterson: 'How can I get this snail out of my ear?'

'Sir, is it true that if you dissolve a policeman in H_2SO_4 you get Copper Sulphate?'

After explaining to little Benjamin that school was somewhere children had to go to until they were sixteen, Mum took him off there for his first day.

As she left him in the classroom he started to cry and called after her, 'Mummy — you *will* come back for me when I'm sixteen, won't you?'

Orson: 'Please, Miss, can I be in the Nativity play, Miss? Can I, Miss . . . Miss, please?'
Teacher: 'Oh, all right, Orson . . . you can be the star.'
Orson: 'Joseph, Miss?'
Teacher: 'No, the star. We'll hang you up above the stage.'

Teacher: 'Kevin, who was the Black Prince's father?'

Kevin: 'Old King Cole, Sir.'

'Which school has the wettest headmaster?'
'A school of fish.'

'Where did Paul Daniels learn most of his tricks?'
'Card school.'

'Where can one learn about belly-buttons?'
    'Navel college.'

'Where do pupils have trouble keeping their desks in one place?'
    'A dancing school.'

'Where did Professor Frankenstein learn his trade?'
    'Life classes.'

'Where do French polishers learn their trade?'
    'Finishing school.'

Maths teacher: 'Peregrine, what is half of nine?'
Peregrine: 'There are two halves, sir. The big half is five and the little half is four.'

Teacher: 'If you divide 986 by 12 and then add 94, what do you have?'
Caroline: 'The wrong answer.'

Teacher: 'If you had twenty pence, and you asked your dad for another twenty pence, how much would you have?'
Wally: 'Twenty pence, Miss.'
Teacher: 'You don't know your arithmetic, Wally.'
Wally: 'And you don't know my dad, Miss!'

Teacher: 'Jeremy, what do we call the thick, dark, crinkly stuff that covers the trunk of a tree?'
Jeremy: 'I don't know, Sir.'
Teacher: 'Bark, boy, BARK!'
Jeremy: 'Bow wow! Bow wow!'

Stanley: 'I wish we had lived a hundred years ago.'
Oliver: 'Why's that?'
Stanley: ' 'Cos there'd have been a lot less history to learn.'

Teacher: 'You are late, Jenkins. You should have been here at nine.'
Jenkins: 'Why, what happened?'

Teacher: 'What are stalagmites?'
Bradshaw: 'Prison camp germs, Sir.'

Dad: 'Do you find anything hard to take in at school?'
Lad: 'Only the dinners.'

Teacher: 'Harold, give me two pronouns.'
Harold: 'Who, me?'
Teacher: 'Quite correct!'

Jimmy: 'Dad, I'm the school swat.'
Dad: 'You . . . the school swat? Never!'
Jimmy: 'I am. I spent all yesterday afternoon killing flies.'

Knock! Knock!
Who's there?
Everett.
Everett who?
Everett anything worse than these school dinners?

Knock! Knock!
Who's there?
Howell.
Howell who?
Howell I ever get my homework done if you lot
don't be quiet?

Knock! Knock!
Who's there?
Andrew.
Andrew who?
Andrew a picture of the teacher on
the blackboard.

Knock! Knock!
Who's there?
Carrie.
Carrie who?
Carrie my bag for me, will you?

Knock! Knock!
Who's there?
Hugh.
Hugh who?
Hugh must be joking! Carry it yourself.

Knock! Knock!
Who's there?
David.
David who?
David my pencil-case and I can't find it
anywhere.

Teacher: 'Jackie . . . late again!'
Jackie: 'It's the bus, Sir . . . it keeps coming
late.'
Teacher: 'All right, but if it's late again in the
morning, you must catch an earlier
one.'

Teacher: 'Does anyone know where Felixstowe
is?'
Darren: 'Inside Felix's sock, Miss.'

Teacher: 'Simon, I'm pleased to be able to tell
you that your writing has improved
tremendously.'
Simon: 'Thank you, Sir.'
Teacher: 'But now I can see just what a terrible
speller you are.'

Teacher: 'Maurice, what is five and five?'
Maurice: 'Ten, Sir.'
Teacher: 'That's good.'
Maurice: 'Good? You can't get a better answer.'

Mr Splurge: 'How old would someone be now if they were born in 1945?'
Dopey: 'Oh . . . er . . . man or woman, Sir?'

Teacher: 'Sally, would you point out New Zealand on the map for me, please?'
Sally: 'There, Sir.'
Teacher: 'Correct. Now, Susan, tell me, who discovered New Zealand?'
Susan: 'Sally did, Sir.'

Teacher: 'Your brother is absent again, Brown. Where is he?'
Brown: 'He's fell running, Sir.'
Teacher: 'Oh, dear! Has he hurt himself?'
Brown: 'I shouldn't think so, he's a very good fell runner.'

Teacher: 'And why were you absent yesterday, Carter?'

Carter: 'I slipped and twisted my ankle, Sir.'

Teacher: 'That's a lame excuse.'

'Why did the strawberry take the day off school?'

'He was feeling a bit seedy.'

'Why did the piece of string take the day off school?'

'He was feeling ropey.'

'Why did Dai (dye) take the day off school?'

'He was feeling off colour.'

Mr Crumb: 'If I gave you two rabbits today, Smith, and then gave you three more tomorrow, how many rabbits would you have?'

Smith: 'Seven, Sir.'

Mr Crumb: 'Seven?'

Smith: 'Yes, Sir, I've got two already.'

Geography Teacher: 'Can anyone tell me where Oldham is?'

Atkinson: 'Second division, Sir.'

Teacher: 'This afternoon I will instruct you on the South American Pampas.'

Albert: 'Will we be back in time for me tea, Sir?'

Teacher: 'If I gave you two rabbits today and then gave you two more tomorrow, how many rabbits would you have?'

Robin: 'Hundreds before very long I should imagine.'

Miss Leeds: 'Andrew, if I say, "I have went", is this correct?'

Andrew: ' 'Course not — you're still here.'

Teacher: 'Sandy, who built the Forth Bridge?'

Sandy: 'No idea, Sir. And I couldn't tell you who built the first three either.'

Mr Mapp: 'Johnson, name me a country that is very cold.'

Johnson: 'New Zealand.'

Mr Mapp: 'That is incorrect.'

Johnson: 'Then how come their meat is always frozen?'

Mr Brush: 'Harold, I told you to draw a horse and a gypsy caravan, but you've only drawn the horse.'

Harold: 'Yes, Sir, the horse will draw the caravan.'

Smith: 'Sir, should someone be in trouble for something they haven't done?'

Teacher: 'Of course not.'

Smith: 'That's all right then, because I haven't done my homework.'

Colin: 'Sir, if the earth is spinning round, why don't we all drop off?'

Teacher: 'That's because of the Law of Gravity, Colin.'

Colin: 'But what did people do before the government passed the law, Sir?'

'Why are you always late, boy?'

' 'Cos you always start before I get here, Miss.'

Teacher: 'Quick, Thomas . . . the name of a
liquid that won't freeze.'
Thomas: 'Er . . . boiling water, Sir.'

Teacher: 'What is the best way of preventing
food from going bad?'
Muncher: 'Eat it, Miss.'

Teacher: 'I hope I didn't see you looking at
Boswell's exam paper, Dickens!'
Dickens: 'I hope so as well, Sir.'

The headmaster was about to cane Wilkins for
being naughty.
Head: 'Wilkins, bend over. This is going to hurt
me more than it will hurt you.'
Wilkins: 'Shall we change places then, Sir?'

Teacher: 'Can anyone name me something that did not exist fifty years ago?'
Lucy: 'Please, Miss . . . me!'

Mr Crabb: 'And where are you from, O'Reilly?'
New boy: 'Ireland, Sir.'
Mr Crabb: 'What part?'
New boy: 'All of me, Sir.'

Teacher: 'What contribution did the Phoenicians make to civilisation?'
Witty: 'They invented those blinds like the ones in the headmaster's office windows.'

Emma: 'Our teacher is very, very special.'
Alison: 'What do you mean?'
Emma: 'She's in a class of her own.'

Teacher: 'Martin, who was the first woman?'
Martin: 'I can't remember, Miss.'
Teacher: 'Come on, boy . . . think . . . think of an apple.'
Martin: '*Now* I remember . . . Granny Smith!'

Teacher: 'Sandra, did your big brother help you with your homework?'
Sandra: 'No, Miss. He did it all.'

Teacher: 'George, this is your handwriting in Warren's notebook. You've been doing his homework for him again, haven't you?'

George: 'No, Sir, but we used the same fountain pen.'

Randolph had been sent out of the class for being naughty and, as it was the last lesson of the day, he decided to go home. Unfortunately, the headmaster saw him.

'And where do you think you are going, boy? There is another ten minutes before the bell.'

'Well, it's like this, Sir,' Randolph said. 'I was late this morning, and I don't believe in being late twice in one day!'

Teacher: 'Peter, what does it mean when the barometer falls?'

Peter: 'The school caretaker has done a lousy job again, Sir.'

Teacher: 'Sidebottom, if I had £10,000 in the bank and £25,000 in the building society, what would I have?'

Sidebottom: 'A pools win, Sir.'

Teacher: 'June, what is the most often used answer to my questions?'
June: 'I don't know, Sir.'
Teacher: 'Quite correct!'

Teacher: 'Blenkinsop, you've got a hole in the seat of your trousers. I hope you'd tell me if you saw a hole in mine.'
Blenks: 'No, Sir, but I'd tell everyone else.'

Teacher: 'Blackwell, will you define "unaware" for me?'
Blackwell: ' 'S what I wear una my clothes, innit?'

Biology teacher: 'What do moths eat?'
Coggins: 'Holes, Miss.'

Boy: 'I got into trouble today for not knowing where the Himalayas were.'
Dad: 'I've told you before. You should remember where you put things.'

Science teacher: 'Which travels quicker, heat or cold?'
Scroggins: 'Must be heat. It's easy to catch a cold.'

Dad was intently watching a football match on the television when his son came running downstairs. 'Dad, Dad, I've swallowed my fountain-pen while I was doing my homework. What should I do?'

Dad didn't take his eyes off the screen. 'Use a pencil,' he answered.

Maths teacher: 'If a mother had seven children and only five potatoes, how would she divide them equally between the children?'

Conrad: 'Make chips, Miss.'

Del: 'If the headmaster doesn't take back what he just said, then I'm leaving this school and not coming back.'

Tel: 'What did he say.'

Del: 'He told me I was expelled.'

Boy: 'Dad, I don't feel like studying tonight. I'm too tired.'

Father: 'Listen, Son, hard work never killed anyone.'

Boy: 'And I don't want to run the risk of being the first.'

Teacher: 'Wally, can you tell me one use for alligator skin?'

Wally: 'Er . . . it's used for keeping the alligator in one piece, Sir.'

Stan: 'If I put four ducks in a packing case, what have I got?'

Teacher: 'I don't know.'

Stan: 'A box of quackers.'

Science teacher: 'In 1771 oxygen was discovered by a Swedish chemist called Scheele.'

Brownlow: 'Sir, what did people breathe before then?'

Teacher: 'Why are you so late, Penelope?'
Penny: 'I was stopped by a tramp on my way to school. He said he hadn't had a bite all week.'
Teacher: 'Did you give him your lunch?'
Penny: 'No, I bit him.'

Mr Crabb: 'This note concerning your absence yesterday, Wayne . . . are you sure this is your mother's signature?'
Wayne: 'Oh, yes, Sir . . . this is the pen I used.'

'I can't understand it, bad tempers seem to be all the rage amongst the teachers, this week.'

Matron: 'What's the best thing to take when you are run down?'
Pupil: 'The registration number of the car.'

Mr Summit: 'Geoffrey, if you bought seventy pears for thirty-five pence, what would each one be?'
Geoff: 'At that price – rotten!'

Gran: 'How do you like school, Eddie?'
Eddie: 'Shut.'

A daft science student called Pye,
Thought making explosives he'd try.
With a room full of vapour,
He lit up a taper,
And now we have Pye in the sky.

Said a muscular tomboy called Jean,
'On netball I'm not really keen.
It's played with such grace,
I feel right out of place.
Can't I try for the rugby fifteen?'

Maxie: 'What's that smell, Miss?'
Dinner lady: 'I've made the chicken soup.'
Maxie: 'Thank goodness for that — I thought it
was for us.'

Sally: 'It was our form teacher's birthday last
week and they fired a twenty-one gun
salute.'
Sue: 'Yes?'
Sally: 'Yes, but every one of them missed!'

First teacher: 'There are two things I hate about
young Spotty Scroggins. His
behaviour is absolutely appalling.'
Second teacher: 'What's the second thing?'
First teacher: 'He's never absent.'

An old woodwork teacher called Friend,
By his pupils was sent round the bend.
One day around two,
They covered his chair with glue,
And he came to a real sticky end.

Boris: 'Are you still learning the banjo?'
Maurice: 'Yes, but my playing is not very good.'
Boris: 'It'll get better if you pick it.'

Head: 'I think it's time I had a chat to your
parents, Parsons. Do you think they'd
mind if I dropped in?'
Parsons: ' 'Course not, Sir. We live on a
houseboat.'

Myrtle: 'Did you say that you learned to play the
piano after just six easy lessons, Miss?'
Teacher: 'Yes, Myrtle, just six easy lessons —
and about a thousand really hard ones.'

Woodwork master: 'That piece of wood is no good for the table you are making, Simmons. Those are knot holes.'

Simmons: 'They look like holes to me, Sir.'

Teacher: 'Beryl, why are you late?'

Beryl: 'Because my brother beat me up this morning.'

Teacher: 'He beat you up?'

Beryl: 'Yes, Sir. I usually beat him up and get in the bathroom first.'

Caretaker: 'Right then — who broke that window?'

Orson: 'He did, Sir — Walters.'

Caretaker: 'How did he do that?'

Orson: 'I threw a stone at him and he moved.'

Jennifer: 'Why does it rain, Miss?'

Teacher: 'To make all the flowers and trees grow.'

Jennifer: 'Why does it rain on the road then?'

Teacher: 'To make the cars go "bloom-bloom", of course!'

Linda: 'That Darren from 4B is really annoying me.'

Mandy: 'But he's not even looked at you.'

Linda: 'That's what's annoying me!'

Peter: 'Our chemistry teacher, Smelly Sloane, has invented a chemical that will eat its way through anything.'

Rick: 'Yeah?'

Peter: 'Yes – now he's trying to invent something to put it in.'

Gill: 'Our school band only plays country music.'

Clare: 'Why's that?'

Gill: 'Because of the racket we make — they won't let us play in town.'

Bright infant: 'Ever since I can remember, my mummy and daddy have been teaching me to walk and talk. Now this lot keep telling me to sit down and be quiet!'

Teacher: 'How did you sprain your ankle?'

John: 'Did you see that hole that the workmen have dug near the school gate?'

Teacher: 'Yes.'

John: 'I didn't.'

'Why did you push your bike all the way to school this morning?'
   'I set off so late I didn't have time to get on.'

'What happens to the schoolboy who misses the train?'
   'He catches it when he gets to school.'

Boris: 'What did your dad say when you told him you had finished at the bottom of the class?'
Fred: 'He took it like a lamb.'
Boris: 'Yes?'
Fred: 'Yes — he said "Baa"!'

Mum: 'Teddy, aren't you up yet? You are going to be late for school.'
Teddy: 'Sorry, Mum — I dreamt I was playing in the Cup Final and we went into extra time.'

Dad: 'Stop worrying about your school clothes, Ian. When I was your age, my mother used to buy my clothes from the Army and Navy Store. How would you like to have to go to school dressed as a Japanese admiral!?'

P.E. teacher: 'Simon, you have no competitive spirit whatsoever. Have you never come first in anything?'

Simon: 'Yes, Sir. I was the first in the class to get mumps.'

P.E. teacher: 'Bacon, while you are carrying all that weight you'll never win anything. I'll bet you don't know what it's like to finish first.'

Porky: 'Oh, yes I do. You ask any of the kids who sit at my table at lunchtime.'

Head: 'Wilcox, I'm told you stayed off school yesterday to play cricket. Is that true?'

Wilcox: 'No, Sir — and I've got three rainbow trout to prove it.'

Teacher: 'You are leaving school today, Masters. Have you any regrets?'

Masters: 'Just one. I'm sorry I had to come at all.'

George: 'Right then — we'll toss for it. Heads we play football, tails we go to the baths.'

Bobby: 'What about our homework?'

George: 'If the coin doesn't come back down when I toss it, we'll stay in and do our homework.'

Teacher: 'Sean, if I had thirty pebbles in my left trouser pocket and forty pebbles in my right trouser pocket, what would I have?'

Sean: 'Broken braces, Sir.'

Teacher: 'Millicent, can you tell me what a graph is?'

Millicent: 'Yes, Miss, it's an animal with a very long neck.'

Dad: 'What happened at school today, Son?'
Son: 'The bishop came on a visit and he blessed me.'
Dad: 'Really.'
Son: 'Yes, and I hadn't even sneezed!'

Teacher: 'What was the name of Noah's wife?'
Freddie: 'Joan of Arc, Miss.'

'What has twenty two legs, goes around screaming and cries when it is beaten?'
'The school hockey team.'

'Please, Sir, why am I always in the third team?'
'Because we haven't got a fourth.'

Teacher: 'Grenville, name me two of the four seasons.'

Grenville: 'Salt and vinegar.'

Teacher: 'Josie, give me another name for the Dog Star.'

Josie: 'Lassie.'

Mum: 'Sammy, your school reports used to be much better than this.'

Sammy: 'I know, but don't blame me, blame the teacher.'

Mum: 'What do you mean?'

Sammy: 'Well, I used to sit next to Brainy Brightwell and teacher's gone and moved him.'

Cookery teacher: 'That's it, Jennie, you are banned from cookery from now on.'

Jennie: 'But, Miss, I'm not the first to burn something.'

Teacher: 'You're the first to burn the classroom down.'

Teacher: 'Adams, when is the best time to pick apples?'

Adams: 'When the bloke who owns the orchard has gone out.'

Rodney: 'Dad, I'm the teacher's pet.'

Dad: 'She must like you a lot, Son.'

Rodney: 'Not really; she keeps me in a cage!'

Teacher: 'Midwood, why do birds fly south in winter?'

Midwood: 'Too far for them to walk, Sir.'

Teacher: 'Lotte, what is the Order of the Bath?'

Lotte: 'Well, first it's little Willy, then the twins, then me . . .'

Mickey: 'I hate going to that rotten old school.'
Dad: 'Nonsense! Schooldays are the happiest days of your life.'
Mickey: 'Then there's not a lot to look forward to!'

Mr Additt: 'Patrick, how many legs has a horse?'
Patrick: 'Six, Sir.'
Mr Additt: 'Six?'
Patrick: 'Forelegs at the front and two at the back.'

Arnold: 'Dad, I won the hundred metres at the school sports.'
Dad: 'Well done, Son. What did you do it in?'
Arnold: 'Me shorts an' me trainers.'

Teacher: 'James, can you tell me something about Rasputin?'
James: 'No, Sir, I've never rasputed.'

Teacher: 'Jones . . . you're late.'
Jones: 'I'm sorry, Sir, I usually wake at the crack of dawn, but this morning I didn't hear it go off.'

Headmaster: 'On Monday I will be introducing corporal punishment.'
Daft teacher: 'Oh, super. Will he be telling us about life in the army?'

Chemistry teacher: 'What is the chemical symbol for Barium?'
Greenwood: 'Ba, Sir.'
Teacher: 'And the symbol for Sodium?'
Greenwood: 'Na, Sir.'
Teacher: 'What would we get if we added one Barium molecule to two Sodium molecules?'
Greenwood: 'A banana, Sir!'

Gordon: 'If I hadn't been keeping goal for the school team today, they'd have lost twenty–nil.'
Alice: 'What was the score then?'
Gordon: 'Nineteen–nil.'

Tug: 'Dad, the headmaster sent me home and told me to ask you something.'
Dad: 'Ask me what?'
Tug: 'What does expelled mean?'

Atkins: 'Miss, those meat pies were 'orrible.'

Dinner lady: 'Don't be cheeky, Atkins. I was making those pies before you were born.'

Atkins: 'Well, it's time you made some fresh ones then.'

Rocky: 'Dad. I've been suspended from the school.'

Dad: 'How long for?'

Rocky: 'Just for today.'

Dad: 'That's not very long.'

Rocky: 'It is when you're on the end of a rope!'

Jenkins limped into matron's room after falling down the stairs. 'Did you miss a step?' she asked.

'No, Matron,' replied Jenkins. 'I hit every one of them!'

Spiggott: 'Dad, I've been asked to leave the school.'
Dad: 'What for?'
Spiggott: 'For good!'

Biology teacher: 'It is possible for a human being to live for a couple of weeks on water.'
Benson: 'Sir, my dad lived for seven months on water.'
Teacher: 'That's impossible.'
Benson: 'It's not, Sir. He was in the Navy.'

Teacher: 'What is an exporter?'
Sarah: 'Please, Sir, it's someone who used to work for British Rail.'

Boy: 'Is it hard to become as clever as you?'
University Don: 'No — not if you do it by degrees.'

Teacher: 'What does posthumous mean?'
Albert: 'It's a book written by an author after
　　　　　he's dead, Sir.'

'What is heavy water?'
　'The stuff you have to carry from the tap to the
caravan on a campsite.'

Headmaster: 'Now, Lionel, why were you
　　　　　　　throwing stones at that boy from
　　　　　　　the fifth form?'
Lionel: 'He threw them at me first.'
Head: 'Then you should have come and told me.'
Lionel: 'Why? I bet you can't throw stones any
　　　　　better than me.'

Teacher: 'And I have found that lemon juice is extremely beneficial to the complexion.'

Katy (whispering): 'No wonder she's such a sourpuss!'

Headmaster: 'Who gave you that black eye, boy?'

Tug: 'Nobody gave it to me, Sir. I had to fight to get it.'

Mum: 'Jonathan, your clothes are filthy. What happened?'

Jonathan: 'I tried to stop a boy getting beaten up at school.'

Mum: 'Who?'

Jonathan: 'Me.'

Teacher: 'Who was Marconi?'
Sparks: 'Pa Coni's wife, Sir.'

Teacher: 'You lot don't know how lucky you are
having a school bus. When I was your
age I had to get up at six thirty and
walk seven miles to school, and
thought nothing of it.'
Smiffy: 'I wouldn't think much of it, either!'

P.E. teacher: 'Arbuckle, have you got your
football boots on yet?'
Arbuckle: 'Yes, Sir — all except one.'

'Luigi Lira?'
   'Present, Miss.'
'Alan Money?'
   'Present.'
'Jimmy Penny?'
   'Present.'
'Tony Pound?'
   'Here, Miss.'
'Sarah Quid?'
   'Present, Miss.'
No wonder she calls it her cash register!

Phil: 'Dad, will you help me with my maths homework?'
Dad: 'No, Son, it wouldn't be right.'
Phil: 'Well, at least you could try!'

Tyrannosaurus Rex sat his 'O' Level in history and passed with extinction.

Dad: 'How was the chemistry exam?'
Son: 'There were twenty questions and I only got one of them wrong.'
Dad: 'That's excellent.'
Son: 'Not really, Dad, I couldn't do the other nineteen.'

Dad: 'This report is awful, Willy. Twentieth in a class of twenty!'
Willy: 'Could have been worse.'
Dad: 'How?'
Willy: 'There could have been more in the class.'

Dad: 'Did you learn anything new at school today?'
Son: 'Yes, Dad, I learned that the homework you did for me was all wrong.'

Teacher: 'What did I say I would do if I caught you talking in class again?'
Dimb: 'Don't know, Sir — I can't remember, either.'

Lois: 'Miss, Stanley has broken my tennis-racket.'
Teacher: 'How did he do that, Lois?'
Lois: 'I hit him with it.'

Dad: 'Kevin, come here at once. This note from your teacher says he finds it impossible to teach you anything.'
Kevin: 'I told you he was useless.'

Dad: 'I'm not at all happy with this report, Son.'
Son: 'I told my teacher you wouldn't be, but he
insisted on sending it anyway.'

Mother: 'Do you know Alison Dean?'
Daughter: 'Yes, Mum. She sleeps next to me in
the Latin class.'

'Can anyone give me an example of a very long
sentence?'
'Life imprisonment, Sir.'

Lesley: 'Miss, it says in the Bible that we are made from dust and to dust we shall return.'

R.I. teacher: 'Yes, Lesley?'

Lesley: 'Well, I looked under my bed this morning and there's somebody either coming or going there!'

'Tell me something about Good Friday.'
'He was saved by Robinson Crusoe.'

'Give me three examples of wholefood.'
'Doughnuts, onion rings and Polo mints.'

Teacher: 'Amanda, I asked you to write out this sentence fifty times to improve your terrible handwriting. Why have you only written it forty four times?'

Amanda: 'I'm terrible at arithmetic as well.'

Dad: 'How did you get on at school today?'

Errol: 'I got nine hundred out of a thousand.'

Dad: 'Is that marks in an exam?'

Errol: 'No, our teacher gave the class a total of one thousand lines — and I got 900 of 'em.'

English teacher: 'Mark Gregory, your knowledge of English literature is appalling. Have you read anything?'

Mark: 'Yes, Sir, I have red hair.'

'Name a species of bird usually kept in captivity?'
  'A jail bird.'

Teacher: 'Colin, why have you got your rubber stuck in your ear?'

Colin: 'You said that everything you tell me goes in one ear and out the other. Well, I've blocked the exit.'

Simon: 'Sorry I'm late, Sir. My mum sent Grandad to pick some mushrooms for breakfast and he dropped dead in the garden.'

Teacher: 'Goodness! What did your mother do?'

Simon: 'Oh, she just opened a tin of tomatoes.'

'Sorry I'm late, Miss. My mum had an accident. She was putting some toilet water on her forehead and the seat fell down.'

Dad: 'How did you get on at school today?'

Georgie: 'I've advanced quite a lot, Dad.'

Dad: 'Oh?'

Georgie: 'Yes, Miss made me sit at the front.'

Mr Frost, the music teacher, was playing the organ before assembly. 'I wish he was on the telly,' said Briggsy.

'Why?' asked his pal.

'So we could turn him off,' was the reply.

Art teacher: 'So you enjoyed your holiday in Paris, Mike. What did you think of the Louvre?'

Mike: 'Well, the one in the hotel was okay . . .'

Teacher: 'And are there any other children in your family?'

New pupil: 'Yes, Miss — I have three brothers and five sisters.'

Teacher: 'Nine altogether!'

New pupil: 'No, Miss, they had us one at a time.'

Teacher: 'Do you think that television programmes can affect our behaviour?'

Morgan: 'Yes, Sir. When *Panorama* comes on it sends me round the twist and me dad round the pub.'

Pupil: 'Shall I play a scale in A flat?'

Music teacher: 'Play it anywhere — anywhere but here.'

Maurice: 'Miss, everybody in the class is calling me Bighead.'

Teacher: 'Take no notice, Maurice. Oh, it's raining! Be a good boy and go and cover my bike with your cap.'

Timothy: 'I sent a photograph of our teacher to a lonely hearts club.'

Sarah: 'What happened?'

Timothy: 'They sent it back and said nobody was that lonely.'

Pupil: 'Sir, do you think I should take up the piano as a career?'

Music teacher: 'No, I think you should put down the lid as a favour.'

Miss Crumb: 'Class, I have something to tell you. Mr Ward has announced that he is going to marry the most beautiful girl in the world.'

Wharton: 'What a rotten shame! You and him have been engaged all that time, as well!'

Sidebottom: 'Sorry I missed that open goal, Sir. I could kick myself.'

P.E. teacher: 'Don't try to — you'd miss.'

Lightfoot: 'Sir, why do the other players in the team keep calling me Cinderella?'

Teacher: 'It's because you keep running away from the ball.'

Jones: 'Sir, you're biased. You shouldn't be refereeing this football match.'

Teacher: 'Don't be impertinent, Jones. Any more lip and I won't let you play against us again.'

Chemistry teacher: 'Who has lit this bunsen burner?'

Mills: 'Oh, some bright spark.'

Pupil: 'Sir, there's a naked piano in the music room.'

Music Teacher: 'Idiot! That's the new harp!'

Pryce: 'Sir, I'd like to be an auctioneer when I leave school. What do I need to know?'

Teacher: 'Lots!'

P.E. teacher: 'I've arranged a tug o' war contest against East Street Comprehensive school this afternoon. Any volunteers?'

Makepiece: 'Me, Sir. But I have a question.'

P.E. teacher: 'Well?'

Makepiece: 'East Street is seven miles away — have we got a rope that long?'

Johnny: 'What are you digging that hole for, Mr Grouch?'
Caretaker: 'I'm burying my canary.'
Johnny: 'That's a big hole for a canary.'
Caretaker: 'It's inside the headmaster's cat!'

'The school dinners aren't that bad.'

'Oh, no? They're treating the dustbins for food poisoning!'

Teacher: 'What is the staple diet of the Russians?'
Jones: 'Minsk meat, Sir.'

Teacher: 'Where was the trampoline invented?'
Miles: 'Alice Springs.'

Teacher: 'A lot of discoveries were made by accident . . .'
Kieron: 'Yes, Sir, that's how me dad discovered that Mum couldn't drive!'

Teacher: 'What are doubloons?'
Wally: 'Daft twins, Sir.'

A stupid old duffer called Tree,
Taught chemistry, art and P.E.,
His experiments stunk,
His paintings were junk,
And press-ups he managed just three.

Teacher: 'When was the Magna Carta signed?'
Samantha: 'Quarter past twelve, Miss.'
Teacher: 'Quarter past twelve?'
Samantha: 'Yes, Miss — 1215 to you.'

Dennis: 'I've just seen two of the school
cleaning-ladies dancing.'
Maud: 'What were they doing?'
Dennis: 'The char-char.'

Father: 'Gerry, your history teacher informs me
that you are the worst pupil in her class.'
Gerry: 'It's not my fault, Dad, she keeps asking
questions about things that happened
before I was born.'

'My parents think that nine years old is too young to be going out with boys. But don't worry — it's just a phase they're going through.'

Sign in the Junior section of the public library: HUSH, HUSH, WHISPER WHO DARES.

Jimmy arrived home from school covered from head to toe in dirty, stinking mud. 'Mum, I've found a terrific short cut home from school!'

Knock! Knock!
Who's there?
Columbine.
Columbine who?
Columbine a new bike with your birthday money.

Knock! Knock!
Who's there?
Colette.
Colette who?
Colette my sweets, the greedy pig.

Knock! Knock!
Who's there?
Betta.
Betta who?
Betta get a move on, we're late for school.

Knock! Knock!
Who's there?
Hildegarde.
Hildegarde who?
Hildegardes the goals when we play hockey.

Knock! Knock!
Who's there?
Jennifer.
Jennifer who?
Jennifer her extra maths tuition, Sir.

Knock! Knock!
Who's there?
Letitia.
Letitia who?
Letitia is French for the teacher . . . I think!

Maths teacher: 'If the average car is three metres long, and three thousand of them were placed end to end . . .'

Bloggs: 'That would be the M55 into Blackpool on a Bank Holiday.'

Tommy: 'My uncle disappeared when he was on a hunting trip.'

Teacher: 'What happened to him?'

Tommy: 'Mum says that something he disagreed with ate him.'

Gordon: 'Sir, is it true that a road sweeper sweeps roads?'

Teacher: 'Yes.'

Gordon: 'And a weight-lifter lifts weights?'

Teacher: 'Yes.'

Gordon: 'Then does a shoplifter lift shops?'

Teacher: 'Can somebody tell me where polar bears can be found?'

Pat: 'I didn't know they were lost, Sir.'

Teacher: 'William, give me an example of a double negative.'

William: 'I don't know none, Sir.'

Teacher: 'Correct.'

Teacher: 'Helen, do you know how to spell cough?'

Helen: 'C-o-f-f.'

Teacher: 'The dictionary spells it c-o-u-g-h.'

Helen: 'You didn't ask me how the dictionary spells it.'

Teacher: 'Why are the Middle Ages sometimes called the Dark Ages?'

Arthur: 'Because they had so many knights, Sir.'

Brian: 'Sir, I was eating an apple at lunch time and I swallowed a worm.'

Teacher: 'Go to the school nurse. She'll give you something for it.'

Brian: 'No, thanks. I'll just let it starve.'

Teacher: 'How did you get that swelling on your nose?'

Mavis: 'I bent down to smell a brose.'

Teacher: 'There's no "b" in rose.'

Mavis: 'There was in this one.'

Bernard: 'A steam-roller ran over my aunty.'

Teacher: 'That's terrible. What did you do?'

Bernard: 'I took her home and slipped her under the door.'

Teacher: 'What is a cannibal?'

Mickey: 'I don't know, Sir.'

Teacher: 'Well, if you ate your mother and father, what would you be?'

Mickey: 'An orphan.'

Teacher: 'Martin, are you an only child?'

Martin: 'Yes, Sir.'

Teacher: 'Thank goodness for that!'

Teacher: 'Why did you put a frog in Mary's bag, Billy?'

Billy: 'Because I couldn't find a spider, Miss.'

Teacher: 'What can you tell me about the Iron Age?'

Peter: 'Sorry, Sir – I'm a bit rusty on that.'

Teacher: 'Where was the Magna Carta signed?'

Johnny: 'At the bottom, Miss.'

Sports teacher: 'What are the best vegetables for
athletes to eat?'
Alison: 'Runner beans, Sir.'

Headmaster: 'Now, Class 3B, I'd like to
introduce you to your new cookery
teacher. This is Mr Mike O'Wave.'

Teacher: 'What is the most important thing you learn in chemistry, Peter?'

Peter: 'Never to lick the spoon, Sir.'

Teacher: 'Where is your biology book, Johnson?'

Johnson: 'In the bin, Sir.'

Teacher: 'What's it doing in there?'

Johnson: 'Well you kept writing "Rubbish" all over it.'

Teacher: 'And what's your name?'

Simon: 'Simon!'

Teacher: 'Say "Sir" when you talk to me.'

Simon: 'Okay! Sir Simon.'

Frank: 'We bumped into our teacher at the shops yesterday.'

Penny: 'Was she pleased to see you?'

Frank: 'Not really. Dad wasn't looking where he was driving at the time.'

Aunty Clara: 'Do you like going to school, Nigel?'

Nigel: 'Yes, I like going to school and I like coming back – but I don't really like the bit in the middle.'

Teacher: 'Why did Robin Hood rob the rich?'
Paul: 'Because the poor didn't have any money to steal.'

Teacher: 'On average, it takes three sheep to make one jumper.'
Sally: 'I didn't even know sheep could knit, Miss.'

History teacher: 'What's a Roman urn?'
Silly Simon: 'About £90 a week, Sir.'

'What do you call a teacher with a rabbit down his trousers?'
   'Warren.'

Teacher: 'If you had four bananas and ate one,
how many would you have?'
James: 'Four.'
Teacher: 'Four?'
James: 'Yes. Three outside and one inside.'

Teacher: 'Although birds are very small, they
are very clever creatures. What can a
bird do that I can't?'
Laura: 'Have a bath in a bowl, Miss.'

Teacher: 'Spell "battle", Karen.'
Karen: 'B-A-T-T-T-L-E.'
Teacher: 'Leave out one of the Ts.'
Karen: 'Which one, Sir?'

'What do you call a teacher whose car has got
four flat tyres?'
'Carlo.'

Murphy: 'On the school bus this morning, a little
boy fell off his seat and everybody
laughed at him, except me.'
Teacher: 'Which little boy was it?'
Murphy: 'Me.'

Teacher: 'Mark, if you had seven sweets and Ian asked you for one, how many would you have left?'

Mark: 'Seven.'

'What do you call a teacher who is always in debt?'

'Owen.'

Headmaster: 'Do you have any unusual pupils in your class?'

Teacher: 'Yes, two of them have good manners.'

Teacher: 'Scott, why are you so late this morning?'

Scott: 'Every step I walked forward, I slipped back two.'

Teacher: 'If that were true, you wouldn't be here now.'

Scott: 'But I turned around and walked backwards, Sir.'

Teacher: 'Sharon, can you tell me what the leading cause of dry skin is?'

Sharon: 'Er, bath towels, Miss.'

Teacher: 'When I was your age, I could name all the kings and queens – and in the correct order.'

Cheeky Charlie: 'But in those days there were only four or five of them, Sir.'

Teacher: 'Now, we all know we should try and conserve energy. Name one way we can do this, Tommy.'

Tommy: 'By staying in bed all day, Sir.'

Teacher: 'Jennifer, what are you drawing?'

Jennifer: 'A picture of God.'

Teacher: 'But nobody knows what God looks like.'

Jennifer: 'They will when I've finished my picture, Miss.'

'What do you call a teacher with a black eye?'
  'Bruce.'

Teacher: 'If you insist on talking, Henry, I'll have to send you to the headmaster's office.'

Henry: 'Oh, does the headmaster want somebody to talk to?'

Did you hear about the girl who had to do a project on trains?

She had to keep track of everything.

Mrs Brown: 'What position does your David have in the school football team?'
Mrs Pearce: 'I think he's one of the drawbacks.'

Music teacher: 'Who can tell me the name of their favourite musical instrument?'
Alec: 'The dinner bell, Miss.'

Teacher: 'Where does your mother come from, Julie.'
Julie: 'Alaska.'
Teacher: 'Don't bother. I'll ask her myself.'

Teacher: 'What do we usually use to conduct electricity?'
Dion: 'Why – er . . .'
Teacher: 'That's right, wire. Now tell me what is the unit we use to measure electrical power?'
Dion: 'The what, Sir?'
Teacher: 'Correct. The watt.'

'What do you call a teacher with a paper bag on his head?'

'Russell.'

'Did you hear about the class of children from a city school who went on a field trip to the country? They found a crate of milk bottles and thought they had stumbled across a cow's nest!'

Teacher: 'Why do salmon swim upstream to spawn?'

Emily: 'Because walking along the river bank hurts their tails.'

Penelope: 'I own 250 goldfish.'

Teacher: 'Where do you keep them all?'

Penelope: 'In the bath.'

Teacher: 'What do you do when you want to have a bath?'

Penelope: 'I blindfold them.'

'What's the difference between school tapioca pudding and frogspawn?'
   'Not a lot!'

Teacher: 'Where would you find your heart, Steven?'
Steven: 'Straight down my throat and take the first turning on the left.'

Teacher: 'Joey, if you don't stop playing that mouth organ you're going to drive me insane.'
Joey: 'Too late, Sir. I stopped over an hour ago!'

Teacher: 'I once had to live on a can of baked beans for four days.'
Boy: 'Wow! Weren't you scared of falling off?'

Teacher: 'Tamsin, what is the first thing you should do with a barrel of crude oil?'
Tamsin: 'Teach it some manners, Sir.'

Teacher: 'Susan, why don't you want to come on our field trip to study insects?'
Susan: 'Because they bug me.'

Linda: 'Miss, is it correct to say that you water a horse?'

Teacher: 'Yes.'

Linda: 'Well, when I get home, I'm going to milk the cat.'

'What do you call a teacher with a seagull on his head?'

'Cliff.'

English teacher: 'This term we are going to study Kipling. Do you like Kipling, Jane?'

Jane: 'I don't know, Miss. I've never kippled.'

Maths teacher: 'Add 3765 to 5341, divide by 2.5, subtract 2779 and multiply by 3.7. What answer have you got?'

Donald: 'The wrong one, Sir.'

Teacher: 'We all know that Alexander Graham Bell invented the telephone. Edgar, what did his assistant, Mr Watson do?'

Edgar: 'He sent out the telephone bills.'

Peter was lolling about in his chair with his feet stuck out in the aisle, chewing bubble gum in the middle of a physics lesson. The teacher noticed and angrily shouted, 'Peter, take that bubble gum out of your mouth and put your feet in, this instant.'

Teacher: 'How many letters are there in the alphabet?'
Melanie: 'Eleven, Miss.'
Teacher: 'Why do you say eleven?'
Melanie: 'Because there are three in "the" and eight in "alphabet".'

History teacher: 'What was Camelot famous for?'
Jimmy: 'Its knight life, Sir.'

Tommy (sniffing): 'It smells like UFO for school dinners today.'
Fred: 'What's UFO?'
Tommy: 'Unidentified frying objects.'

Teacher: 'With your bad cold you should avoid draughts, William.'
William: 'Can I play Scrabble instead?'

'What do you get if you cross an elephant with a caretaker?'
    'A twenty-ton school cleaner.'

'Did you hear about the teacher who dreamt he was eating a giant marshmallow?'
    'He woke up and found he was eating his pillow.'

Teacher: 'Why do giraffes have such long necks?'
Barney: 'Because their feet smell, Miss.'

'What do you call a teacher who has a loud voice?'
    'Mike.'

'Did you hear about the teacher who got a fly in his soup?'
    'He said it must have committed insecticide.'

Geography teacher: 'What makes the Tower of Pisa lean?'
Frank: 'Nobody feeds it.'

Kate: 'This ointment makes my arm smart.'
Teacher: 'In that case, you'd better rub some on your head as well.'

Teacher: 'Can you tell me what a forum is, Ernie?'
Ernie: 'It's a two-um plus two-um.'

English teacher: 'Tony, please don't hum whilst reading your set book.'
Tony: 'I'm not reading, Sir. Just humming.'

'What do you call a teacher who has a stick tied to his leg?'
    'Rodney.'

Art teacher: 'I'd like you to tell me all you know about the famous eighteenth-century painters, Michael.'
Michael: 'They're all dead, Sir.'

The chemistry teacher was trying to teach the class about how acid can dissolve things. He took a £1 coin from his pocket.

'I am going to drop this coin into a beaker of acid,' he said. 'Do you think it will dissolve?'

'I'm sure it won't,' shouted Cheeky Charlie from the back of the class.

'Why are you so sure?' asked the chemistry teacher.

'Because if that coin was going to dissolve you'd never have put it in the beaker!' came the reply.

'What do you call a teacher who comes from Wales and has a biscuit on his head?'

'Dai Gestive.'